Meet the family

compiled by *Sally Grindley*

pictures by *Jo Burroughes*

ORCHARD BOOKS

For my parents
J. B.

For Angela
S. G.

First published in Great Britain in 1990 by
ORCHARD BOOKS
96 Leonard Street, London EC2A 4RH
Orchard Books Australia
14 Mars Road, Lane Cove, NSW 2066
1 85213 191 8
A CIP catalogue record for this book
is available from the British Library.
Printed in Belgium

The compiler and publishers would like to thank the following for permission to reprint the selections in this book. All possible care has been taken to trace the ownership of every selection included and to make full acknowledgment for its use. If any errors have accidentally occurred, they will be corrected in subsequent editions, provided notification is sent to the publishers:
Everybody Says by Dorothy Aldis, reprinted by permission of G. P. Putnam's Sons from *Here, There and Everywhere* by Dorothy Aldis, copyright 1927, 1928, copyright renewed © 1955, 1956 by Dorothy Aldis; The Older the Violin the Sweeter the Tune by John Agard from *Say It Again, Granny*, illustrated by Susanna Gretz, reprinted by permission of The Bodley Head; My Grannies by June Crebbin from *The Jungle Sale*, reprinted by permission of Penguin Books Ltd; Control Calling by Max Fatchen from *Wry Rhymes for Troublesome Times*, reprinted by permission of Penguin Books Ltd; Walking by Aileen Fisher from *Runny Days, Sunny Days*, reprinted by permission of the author; My Gramp by John Foster, first published in *A Second Poetry Book* (Oxford University Press), reprinted by permission of the author; Christmas Thank Yous by Mick Gowar from *Swings and Roundabouts*, reprinted by permission of Collins Publishers; Brother by Mary Ann Hoberman from *Hello and Goodbye*, reprinted by permission of Gina Maccoby Literary Agency copyright © 1959, renewed 1987 by Mary Ann Hoberman; Fishy by Shirley Hughes, first published in *Ten Golden Years* (Walker Books), reprinted by permission of the author; I Have Never Been So Happy by Colin McNaughton from *There's An Awful Lot of Weirdos In Our Neighbourhood*, reprinted by permission of Walker Books; My Sister Laura by Spike Milligan, reprinted by permission of Spike Milligan Productions Ltd; Shed in Space by Gareth Owen from *Song Of The City*, reprinted by permission of Collins Publishers; Guess What Dad Does by Brian Patten from *Gargling With Jelly*, reprinted by permission of Penguin Books and the author; My Uncle Paul of Pimlico by Mervyn Peake from *Rhymes Without Reason*, reprinted by permission of Methuen Children's Books; My Dog, He is an Ugly Dog and My Sister is a Sissy by Jack Prelutsky from *The New Kid on the Block*, copyright © 1984 by Jack Prelutsky, reprinted by permission of Greenwillow Books (A Division of William Morrow and Company Inc.) and Heinemann Young Books; Mother Doesn't Want a Dog by Judith Viorst from *If I Were In Charge of the World and Other Worries*, copyright © 1981 by Judith Viorst, reprinted with permission of Atheneum Publishers, an imprint of Macmillan Publishing Company and Lescher & Lescher; Auntie Agnes's Cat and My Obnoxious Brother Bobby by Colin West from *Not To Be Taken Seriously*, reprinted by permission of Century Hutchinson Ltd; My Little Sister by William Wise, reprinted by permission of William Wise copyright © 1971 William Wise; Give Up Slimming, Mum by Kit Wright from *Rabbiting On*, reprinted by permission of Collins Publishers.

CONTENTS

BROTHER

I had a little brother
And I brought him to my mother
And I said I want another
Little brother for a change.
But she said don't be a bother
So I took him to my father
And I said this little bother
Of a brother's very strange.

But he said one little brother
Is exactly like another
And every little brother
Misbehaves a bit he said.
So I took the little bother
From my mother and my father
And I put the little bother
Of a brother back to bed.

Mary Ann Hoberman

MY SISTER LAURA

My sister Laura's bigger than me
And lifts me up quite easily.
I can't lift her, I've tried and tried;
She must have something heavy inside.

Spike Milligan

MY LITTLE SISTER

My little sister
Likes to eat.
But when she does
She's not too neat.
The trouble is
She doesn't know
Exactly where
The food should go!

William Wise

CONTROL CALLING

Just when I am conducting
A manoeuvre tactical
On my spaceship galactical,
Using my unidentified-object locators,
With my forward disintegrators
Whamming and shooting,
And my astro-clad officers saluting
Amid the rocketry's swirls and swishes,
My sister Kate
Cries 'Activate'
And I'm back on earth,
Drying dishes.

Max Fatchen

MY OBNOXIOUS BROTHER BOBBY

My obnoxious brother Bobby
Has a most revolting hobby;
There, behind the garden wall is
Where he captures creepy-crawlies.

Grannies, aunts and baby cousins
Come to our house in their dozens,
But they disappear discreetly
When they see him smiling sweetly.

For they know as he approaches,
In his pockets are cockroaches,
Spiders, centipedes and suchlike;
All of which they do not much like.

As they head towards the lobby,
Bidding fond farewells to Bobby,
How they wish he'd change his habits
And keep guinea pigs or rabbits.

But their wishes are quite futile,
For he thinks that bugs are cute. I'll
Finish now, but just remind you:
Bobby could be right behind you!

Colin West

9

MY DOG, HE IS AN UGLY DOG

My dog, he is an ugly dog,
he's put together wrong,
his legs are much too short for him,
his ears are much too long.
My dog, he is a scruffy dog,
he's missing clumps of hair,
his face is quite ridiculous,
his tail is scarcely there.

My dog, he is a dingy dog,
his fur is full of fleas,
he sometimes smells like dirty socks,
he sometimes smells like cheese.
My dog, he is a noisy dog,
he's hardly ever still,
he barks at almost anything,
his voice is loud and shrill.

My dog, he is a stupid dog,
his mind is slow and thick,
he's never learned to catch a ball,
he cannot fetch a stick.
My dog, he is a greedy dog,
he eats enough for three,
his belly bulges to the ground,
he is the dog for me.

Jack Prelutsky

MY SISTER IS A SISSY

My sister is a sissy,
she's afraid of dogs and cats,
a toad can give her tantrums,
and she's terrified of rats,
she screams at things with stingers,
things that buzz, and things that crawl,
just the shadow of a spider
sends my sister up the wall.

A lizard makes her shiver,
and a turtle makes her squirm,
she positively cringes
at the prospect of a worm,
she's afraid of things with feathers,
she's afraid of things with fur,
she's scared of almost everything
how come I'm scared of her?

Jack Prelutsky

MOTHER DOESN'T WANT A DOG

Mother doesn't want a dog.
Mother says they smell,
And never sit when you say sit,
Or even when you yell.
And when you come home late at night
And there is ice and snow,
You have to go back out because
The dumb dog has to go.

Mother doesn't want a dog.
Mother says they shed,
And always let the strangers in
And bark at friends instead,
And do disgraceful things on rugs,
And track mud on the floor,
And flop upon your bed at night
And snore their doggy snore.

Mother doesn't want a dog.
She's making a mistake.
Because, more than a dog, I think
She will not want this snake.

Judith Viorst

13

GIVE UP SLIMMING, MUM

My Mum
is short
and plump
and pretty
and I wish
she'd give up
slimming.

So does Dad.

Her cooking's
delicious –
you can't
beat it –
but you really can
hardly bear
to eat it –
the way she sits
with her eyes
brimming,

14

watching you
polish off
the spuds
and trimmings
while she
has nothing

herself but a small
thin dry
diet biscuit:
that's all.

My Mum
is short
and plump
and pretty
and I wish
she'd give up
slimming.

So does Dad.

She says she
looks as though
someone had
sat on her –
BUT WE LIKE MUM
WITH A BIT
OF FAT ON HER!

Kit Wright

GUESS WHAT DAD DOES

When I went to junior school
My friends asked what Dad did.
I did not dare to tell them,
So I had to ad lib.

My father's not a fireman.
He's not a bus conductor.
He's not a stuntman in the films
Or a PE instructor.

Yes he is quite rich,
And no, he's not a banker.
He doesn't own a goldmine
Or an oil tanker.

I help him with his job,
And stay up late at night.
Dad works in the shadows
And does not like the light.

I like his job best of all
And get quite excited
When we enter people's homes
Totally uninvited.

Brian Patten

I HAVE NEVER BEEN SO HAPPY

I have never been so happy
    Since my dear old mom and pappy
Packed the car and left real snappy,
    Said they'd had enough.

I can eat just what I feel like,
    Make up any kind of meal, like
Mars bars, chips and jellied eels, like
    Mommy never made.

To nursery school I gave up going,
    They teach you nothing that's worth knowing,
And anyway there's movies showing
    In the afternoons.

And bedtime, well, it's up to me now,
    Midnight, two or half past three now.
Sometimes I'll just watch TV now
    All night long.

So if you're listening, mom and pappy,
    As you can see I'm really happy
But could you come and change my nappy,
    Mommy, Pappy, please!

Colin McNaughton

WALKING

Father's legs are very long.
He seldom walks for fun.
He mostly walks for getting there,
Which makes ME have to run.

Aileen Fisher

SHED IN SPACE

My Grandad Lewis
On my mother's side
Had two ambitions.
One was to take first prize
For shallots at the village show
And the second
Was to be a space commander.

Every Tuesday
After I'd got their messages,
He'd lead me with a wink
To his garden shed
And there, amongst the linseed
And the sacks of peat and horse manure
He'd light his pipe
And settle in his deck chair.
His old eyes on the blue and distant
That no one else could see,
He'd ask,
'Are we A O.K. for lift off?'
Gripping the handles of the lawn mower
I'd reply:
'A. O.K.'

20

And then
Facing the workbench,
In front of shelves of paint and creosote
And racks of glistening chisels
He'd talk to Mission Control.
'Five-Four-Three-Two-One-Zero-
We have lift off.
This is Grandad Lewis talking,
Do you read me?
Britain's first space shed
is rising majestically into orbit
From its launch pad
In the allotments
In Lakey Lane.'

And so we'd fly,
Through timeless afternoons
Till tea time came,
Amongst the planets
And mysterious suns,
While the world
Receded like a dream:
Grandad never won
That prize for shallots,
But as the captain
Of an intergalactic shed
There was no one to touch him.

Gareth Owen

THE OLDER THE VIOLIN THE SWEETER THE TUNE

Me Granny old
Me Granny wise
stories shine like a moon
from inside she eyes.

Me Granny can dance
Me Granny can sing
but she can't play violin.

Yet she always saying,
'Dih older dih violin
de sweeter de tune.'

Me Granny must be wiser
than the man inside the moon.

John Agard

22

MY GRANNIES

I hate it, in the holiday,
When Grandma brings her pets to stay –
Her goat, her pig, her seven rats
Scare our dog and chase our cats.
Her budgies bite, her parrots shout –
And guess who has to clean them out?

My other Gran, the one I like,
Always brings her motor-bike,
And when she takes me for a ride
To picnic in the countryside,
We zoom up hills and whizz round bends –
I hate it when her visit ends!

June Crebbin

MY GRAMP

My gramp has got a medal.
On the front there is a runner.
On the back it says:
Senior Boys 100 Yards
First William Green
I asked him about it,
but before he could reply
Gran said, 'Don't listen to his tales.
The only running he ever did
was after the girls.'
Gramp gave a chuckle
and went out the back
to get the tea.
As he shuffled down the passage
with his back bent,
I tried to imagine him,
legs flying, chest out,
breasting the tape.
But I couldn't.

Derek Stuart

FISHY

Great Uncle Morissey, Dad and Mum
Were drowsing in deck-chairs in the sun.
'Run off and play,' they said to me,
'Make sand pies till it's time for tea.'

I was fetching some water in my pail
When I came across a lady with a long fishy tail,
Sitting by a pool on a seaweedy shelf,
Singing softly, all by herself.

When I asked if she'd care to take some tea
With Great Uncle Morissey, Dad, Mum and me,
She lashed up the water, shook out her hair,
Sent a thousand droplets into the air,
And I just caught sight of the tip of her fin
As she whisked up her tail and dived right in.

When I asked Uncle Morissey if he would wish
To meet a lady who was half a fish,
He only yawned and said he'd seen plenty
When he was a lad, back in 1920.

Shirley Hughes

MY UNCLE PAUL OF PIMLICO

My Uncle Paul of Pimlico
Has seven cats as white as snow,
Who sit at his enormous feet
And watch him, as a special treat,
Play the piano upside-down,
In his delightful dressing-gown;
The firelight leaps, the parlour glows,
And, while the music ebbs and flows,
They smile (while purring the refrains),
At little thoughts that cross their brains.

Mervyn Peake

AUNTIE AGNES'S CAT

My Auntie Agnes has a cat.
I do not like to tell her that
Its body seems a little large
(With lots of stripes for camouflage).
Its teeth and claws are also larger
Than they ought to be. A rajah
Gave her the kitten, I recall,
When she was stationed in Bengal.
But that was many years ago,
And kittens are inclined to grow.
So now she has a fearsome cat –
But I don't like to tell her that.

Colin West

CHRISTMAS THANK YOUS

Dear Auntie
Oh, what a nice jumper
I've always adored powder blue
and fancy you thinking of
orange and pink
for the stripes
how clever of you

Dear Uncle
The soap is
terrific
So
useful
and such a kind thought and
how did you guess that
I'd just used the last of
the soap that last Christmas brought

Dear Gran
Many thanks for the hankies
Now I really can't wait for the flu
and the daisies embroidered
in red round the 'M'
for Michael
how
thoughtful of you

Dear Cousin
What socks!
and the same sort you wear
so you must be
the last word in style
and I'm certain you're right that the
luminous green
will make me stand out a mile

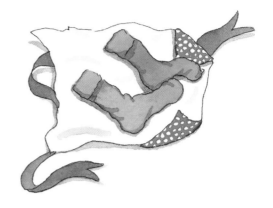

Dear Sister
I quite understand your concern
it's a risk sending jam in the post
But I think I've pulled out
all the big bits
of glass
so it won't taste too sharp
spread on toast

Dear Grandad
Don't fret
I'm delighted
So *don't* think your gift will
offend
I'm not at all hurt
that you gave up this year
and just sent me
a fiver
to spend

Mick Gowar

EVERYBODY SAYS

Everybody says
I look just like my mother.
Everybody says
I'm the image of Aunt Bee.
Everybody says
My nose is like my father's
But I want to look like ME!

Dorothy Aldis